ANDY'S NEW HOUSE

BY SANDRA WIDENER
ILLUSTRATED BY MARY THELEN

Harcourt

Orlando   Boston   Dallas   Chicago   San Diego

Visit *The Learning Site!*

www.harcourtschool.com

Andy and his family are building a new house. Let's see how the workers do it.

Every house starts with many plans. Ronda is sketching the new house. It will be boxy.

Justin and Rusty study every plan. They mark where the house will be on the property. Rusty digs out plenty of rocky dirt.

Now, Randy and Denny make forms. They add water to cement and hurry to put it in the forms.

The squishy cement gets very hard. Harry starts to build the first story floor. He starts in an orderly way.

Next, the workers build the walls. The walls are on the floor when they work. Nailing them up is the tricky part.

One person must hold up the walls. Then another person nails them together. Then the walls make a very sturdy frame.

Harry nails down the floor of
the top story of the house. Andy's
bed will be up on this story.

The workers build the walls
for the top story. Every wall is
very sturdy.

Now, the workers go on the roof above. It must be very strong for windy and chilly days.

Andy's family will need to get into their house soon. They add windows and doors to keep the house warm.

Many workers are in the house now. Denny fits together pipes so water will run.

Other workers paint the walls. They use different paint in different rooms. The room Andy will have is apple red.

Now, the house is set for Andy and his family. They walk in. It's perfect!

Andy and his family like the sunny new house. Many years from now, this will be a very old house. Andy thinks he will still like it.